One day, my Mama and I were walking in the park.
Suddenly Mama stopped, pointed at the ground and said,
"There's a poop log!"

Mama looked very excited as she said,
"I haven't seen one of these for years!"
I was sure I had misheard her. So I asked, "A what, please, Mama?"
"A poop log!" she said again.

"A... ... poop log?" I asked.
"Yes, of course," she said. She stepped off the path and picked up the log.

"Ah-hah!" she exclaimed. "I was right. Look."
She brushed off the snow and showed me the
other side of the log. There was a face on it.

"Let's take it home with us."
Mama tucked the log under her arm
and we carried on walking.

"A poop log?" I asked again, really not understanding. "A log made from poop?" It sounded gross.
"No, silly," laughed Mama. "It's a log that poops!"

That didn't sound any better, really!
Mama explained when Grandma was a little girl in Spain, poop logs were very common. By the 8th of December, most people had put poop logs in their homes. It was part of their Christmas tradition.

Mama said, "They were always about the size of the one I'm carrying. About a foot long, as thick as my leg, and with a face."

Mama told me that sometimes they had four legs!

People will decorate their poop log with a big
smiley face and a little red hat.

Then they would put it close to the fireplace,
or somewhere cozy, like near the Christmas tree,
and cover it with a little blanket.

Then they would feed it every day: little sips of water, yummy cookies, and delicious nuts.

On Christmas Eve, they would take sticks and beat the log, still under its warm blanket, until the log pooped.

"Ew!" I said.
"No," said Mama, smiling. "Not that kind of poop.
Poop logs are special. They poop Christmas treats!"
"Where do poop logs come from?" I asked.

"Well, no one knows for sure. But they say Santa sprinkles a little bit of magic dust as he flies all over the world."

"The trees that the dust lands on
are able to make poop logs."

I was still unsure of the poop log, but it did look better when we gave him a little Santa hat, and his name.

We called him Caga Tió, which means Poop Log,
but it is in Spanish, so it sounds way better.

On Christmas Eve, Mama gave me a stick and showed me how to beat Caga Tió. I didn't like it, but Mama explained that because he's made of wood, the beating felt just like a tickle to him.

And she taught me a funny song to sing too.
When I was nearly finished beating him, Mama asked me to run
to the kitchen to fetch her phone,
so she could take a photo.

Poop, log! Poop for me
And bring me something just for me!
Something small and quite delicious
And I'll stop being so very vicious!

I did that, and then Mama said, "While I record you, carefully lift the blanket and see if Caga Tió has left you anything."

I raised the blanket, very sure that there would
be nothing there... but I was wrong!
There was a big pile of sweets and some toys.

My eyes got so big and my mouth opened so wide, Mama
asked if I was going to swallow Caga Tió whole

After Christmas, Caga Tió vanished. I asked Mama where he was, and she said that every poop log went back to the forest after Christmas to help Santa choose which trees to sprinkle magic dust over to make the poop logs for next year.

I can't wait for Christmas to come again, so we can have another poop log by the tree!

# A Little History Lesson: Caga Tió

The practice of the poop log or Caga Tió comes from ancient Spain, especially the Catalan region. The original log was a rough and ready one, found outside and adapted for the children to feed and beat.

In recent decades, decorating the log has become quite common. You can even buy ready-to-use Caga Tiós at markets and shops in Spain. Traditionally, the log would be burned after Christmas and its ashes recycled to help the crops grow!

The name probably comes from the command, which is sung during the beating, when the log is urged to, 'Poop, log!'

THE CHRISTMAS POOP LOG

ISBN: 978-1-7368211-0-7
Library of Congress Control Number: 2021905859
Printed and bound in China
www.thechristmaspooplog.com

Gold-n-Spike, LLC.
2196 Firestone Trce
Akron, OH 44333 USA
www.gold-n-spike.com

# Adoption Page

This Christmas tradition began for the
_____family on (date) _____.

We have decided to name our Christmas Poop Log
_____.

I, (name)_____ solemnly promise to feed my
Poop Log with nuts and cookies, and to give it water every day until
_____. On _____, I will beat the Log until it poops
out some gifts for me.

I understand the Log is not hurt by the beating, and actually kind of
likes it!

Signed _____